My grandma has gone to heaven

My grandma has gone to heaven

A child's acceptance of death

Alex S Foxhall

CHRISTIAN ART
PUBLISHERS

Published by CHRISTIAN ART PUBLISHERS
P O Box 1599, Vereeniging, 1930

© 1998

First edition 2000
Second edition 2002

Illustrations by Annabelle Nieuwenhuizen
Cover designed by Christian Art Publishers

Set in 16 in 24 pt CarlysHand
by Christian Art Publishers

Printed in Singapore

ISBN 1-86852-929-0

02 03 04 05 06 07 08 09 10 11 – 10 9 8 7 6 5 4 3 2 1

My Grandma has gone to heaven

Peter and his parents were going to the hospital to see Grandma. She had been there for a week now, but this was the first time Peter was going there to visit her. He had made her a special card with

"Get well" written in huge red letters across the front. He had also helped Mum pick some flowers from the garden to take to Grandma.

"Why is Grandma in hospital?" Peter asked as they were leaving home.

Mum smiled at him. "Grandma has a bad heart, and she needs the nurses to look after her," she said.

"Will she get better?" he asked.

"I don't know," replied Mum. "All we can do is pray and ask God to make her well again."

Peter was quiet the rest of the way to the hospital. When they arrived, they went to the front counter. There was a tall nurse dressed all in white standing there.

"Can I help you?" she asked pleasantly.

"We've come to see Mrs Bailey," Dad said softly.

The nurse looked on her computer screen, and then looked back at Dad. "Are you friends or family?" she asked.

"We're family," replied Dad.

"Go right in then," said the nurse. "She's in room 107."

Grandma was lying in a great big bed, with four pillows behind her head. She had a tube coming from her nose, and another one going from her arm to a bag of clear liquid above her head. She seemed to be

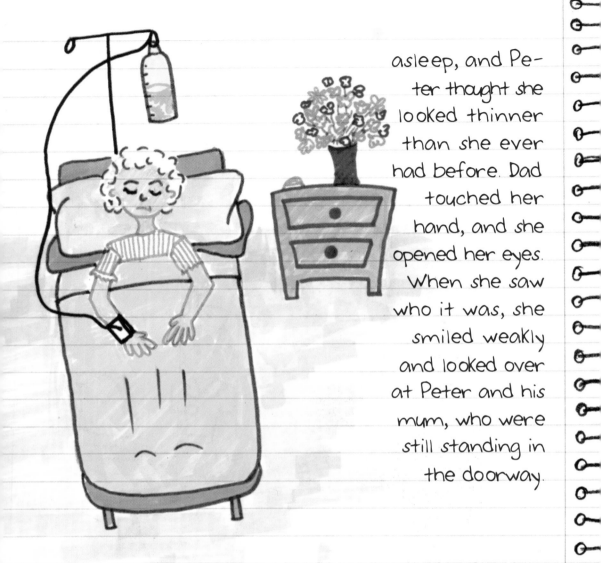

asleep, and Peter thought she looked thinner than she ever had before. Dad touched her hand, and she opened her eyes. When she saw who it was, she smiled weakly and looked over at Peter and his mum, who were still standing in the doorway.

"Hello," she croaked as if she was really thirsty. "I'm so happy to see you."

"It's good to see you too," Mum said softly, although she didn't look very happy. Peter thought he could see tears in her eyes.

Grandma held her hand out, and Peter walked over to her and held it. He didn't like this place very much, and wished that Grandma was back home. Even though the hospital was nice and clean, it was very quiet and smelt like disinfectant.

"Give me a kiss," Grandma whispered. Peter leaned over and kissed her wrinkly cheek.

"I love you, Grandma," he said quietly, and Grandma smiled again. For a second, Peter could see that old sparkle in her eyes, and she looked like the Grandma he used to know. He felt sad to see her so sick.

"Give Grandma the card," Dad told him. Peter had forgotten that he was holding it. He put it into Grandma's hand.

"I haven't got my glasses, dear," said Grandma, sounding a little better now. "Would you mind reading it to me?"

Peter took the card out of Grandma's hand, and read it to her. "'To dear Grandma. Get well. We miss you. Love from Peter.' I drew some flowers on the bottom," he added.

"Thank you, dear," Grandma said. "It's beautiful. Would you please put it on the table over there? I'd like everyone to see it."

"We picked you some flowers," added Mum, holding the bunch near Grandma's face. Grandma took a deep breath through her nose.

"Mmmm, they smell beautiful," she said.

A doctor came in, and asked Dad if he would step outside for a minute. A little while later Dad came back in, looking serious.

"We have to go now, because you need your rest," he told Grandma, kissing her on the forehead. Mum and Peter gave her a kiss too, and then they left. As they walked out of the room, Peter turned to look at Grandma. She was already asleep.

That night, before he went to bed, Peter prayed that God would make Grandma well again. "I really love Grandma, and I know that You love her too," he prayed.

The next morning, Peter awoke to the sound of his

parents talking softly in the kitchen. It was very early, because the sun hadn't even come up yet. Peter got out of bed and went in to the kitchen. Dad and Mum seem- ed surprised to see him, and they both stopped talking.

"How come you're up so early?" asked Peter sleepily.

"Come here, honey," said Mum, reaching out her arms toward him. Peter went over and gave her a hug. He could tell from the way she held him so tightly that something was wrong.

"One of the doctors from the hospital called a little while ago," said Mum at last. "He told us that Grandma has gone to be with Jesus."

"What?" exclaimed Peter. "She's dead?"

Dad nodded sadly, while Mum just started crying. Peter pulled away from Mum's embrace, and looked at them both angrily.

"You're lying!" he yelled at Dad. "She's not dead!" And with that, he ran into his room, threw himself onto his bed, buried his face in his pillow and began to sob loudly. He cried for quite a while, until he finally fell back to sleep.

When he woke up again, Peter felt a lot better. He

went to see Dad, but he was on the phone, talking very seriously to somebody. He found Mum sitting with red eyes in her sewing room, a box of tissues beside her. He knew how she was feeling, because he was feeling it too. He ran over to her and threw his arms around her neck.

"I'm sorry for yelling at Dad," he told Mum tearfully.

"That's okay, honey," Mum replied tenderly. "Dad understands that you were just upset. We all loved Grandma."

"Will I ever see her again?" asked Peter, his tears dropping all over Mum's collar.

"Of course you will, dear," replied Mum. "She'll be the first one to come and give you a hug when you arrive in heaven."

Peter thought about that all day and all that night. Nobody he knew had ever died before, and now he'd have to get used to not visiting Grandma every Sunday after church. Her house would be empty, and all the lollies and chocolates in her cupboard would go mouldy because he wouldn't be there to eat them. He decided he didn't want to wait until he was dead before seeing Grandma again. He felt angry that she was gone.

"Why did You make my grandma die?" he asked God as he was going to sleep that night. "She was a good person, loved by all. Why did she have to die?"

The next morning, Peter got up and went into the dining room to find Dad sitting at the table, reading his Bible.

"Morning, Dad," said Peter unenthusiastically.

"Good morning, Peter," Dad replied, looking up from

his reading. "I'm just reading about how God led the Israelites out of Egypt, with a pillar of cloud by day and a pillar of fire by night. It was Grandma's favourite story."

"Hmph!" Peter mumbled. "If God is so good, why did He take Grandma? I asked Him to make her better, and He didn't."

Dad closed his Bible, and grabbed Peter's hand. "Listen," he said, "do you know where Grandma is now?"

"Probably in one of those freezers for dead people," answered Peter.

"No," Dad corrected, "the real Grandma is in heaven. The bit that's left behind is the part she doesn't need any more. She has a new body now, one that works a whole lot better than the old one."

"Okay," agreed Peter, who had heard it all before but didn't really know whether to believe it or not.

Dad continued. "You remember how she used to miss Grandpa? You probably didn't take much notice, but she really missed him a lot."

"Like I miss her now?" asked Peter.

"More than that. She and Grandpa were married for

over forty years, and it's not easy to live without some-body after you've spent every day with them for so long."

Peter had never thought of that before. He had never heard Grandma accuse God of taking Grandpa away from her. In fact, he once heard her thank God that Grandpa had been a believer, and had gone to heaven.

"Grandma and Grandpa are together today, Peter," Dad went on.

Peter smiled. "I can just imagine it. They would have seen each other as Grandma walked through the gate, and limped over to one another as fast as they could!"

Dad smiled too, and shook his head. "There's no limping in heaven," he said. "They've got new bodies now, and they're in perfect health."

"Has she got her memory back, so she won't keep losing her glasses?" Peter asked, almost laughing as he remembered the way Grandma was always looking for her specs.

"Her memory's perfect, and so is her eyesight. She doesn't wear glasses any more." Dad was roaring with laughter by now, and he and Peter spent the rest of the morning talking and giggling about lovable, forgetful, kind, fussy old Grandma.

"I'm sorry for blaming You," Peter said to God that night. "She's much better off up there with You than down here. At least now she won't keep losing things." He had a sudden thought. "You did answer my prayer after all, didn't You? She's not sick any more," he smiled.

The next day was Grandma's funeral, and Peter was dressed in a black suit with a dark red tie. The church was full of people, most of them old, and Peter sat with his family in the front row. Dad got up to speak about Grandma, and while he was speaking he had to stop several times to blow his nose. When he was nearly finished a tear rolled down his cheek, and Peter realised that Dad was crying. He had never seen his dad cry before, and he realised that Dad must miss Grandma too.

After the service, they all went out to the graveyard, and Grandma's body, inside a huge white coffin, was

lowered into a big rectangular hole. A lady near Peter burst into tears, so Peter told her that Grandma wasn't really inside. "That's just the bit she doesn't need," he explained. "The real Grandma is in heaven."

These days, Peter doesn't miss Grandma like he used to. She is still on his mind a lot, but he's happy to think of her and Grandpa living with Jesus, enjoying their good health and all the wonderful things that heaven has to offer. Like Grandma, he doesn't blame God for taking them from him. Instead, he thanks God every day that Grandma and Grandpa were both believers, and that some day they will all be reunited – Grandpa, Grandma, Dad, Mum and Peter – in a wonderful place prepared for them by Jesus.